CW00522182

VOCAL SCORE

OF

THE

YEOMEN OF THE GUARD;

OR,

THE MERRYMAN AND HIS MAID.

BY

W. S. GILBERT

AND

ARTHUR SULLIVAN.

First published by International Music Publications Ltd
International Music Publications Ltd is a Faber Music company
Bloomsbury House 74–77 Great Russell Street London WC1B 3DA
Printed in England by Caligraving Ltd

ISBN10: 0-571-53560-7
EAN13: 978-0-571-53560-6

THE YEOMEN OF THE GUARD;

OR,

THE MERRYMAN AND HIS MAID.

Dramatis Personæ.

SIR RICHARD CHOLMONDELEY (*Lieutenant of the Tower*)
COLONEL FAIRFAX (*under sentence of death*)
SERGEANT MERYLL (*of the Yeomen of the Guard*)
LEONARD MERYLL (*his Son*)
JACK POINT (*a Strolling Jester*)
WILFRED SHADBOLT (*Head Jailor and Assistant Tormentor*)
THE HEADSMAN
FIRST YEOMAN
SECOND ,,
FIRST CITIZEN
SECOND ,,
ELSIE MAYNARD (*a Strolling Singer*)
PHŒBE MERYLL (*Sergeant Meryll's Daughter*)
DAME CARRUTHERS (*Housekeeper to the Tower*)
KATE (*her Niece*)

Chorus of Yeomen of the Guard, Gentlemen, Citizens, &c.

SCENE .. .. **Tower Green.**

Date.—16th Century.

THE YEOMEN OF THE GUARD.

CONTENTS.

The Yeomen of the Guard;
or,
THE MERRYMAN AND HIS MAID.

Written by
W. S. GILBERT.

Composed by
ARTHUR SULLIVAN.

OVERTURE.

Chappell & Co. Ltd., 50, New Bond Street, London, New York, Sydney

Clar.
p
Viol. & Fag.
Ob.
Viol.
p
p
Ob.
p
Fl.

Viol.
p
Brass.
pp
Viol.
p
cresc.
f
sf
ff TUTTI.
Ped.

Strings.
pp
Clar.
Ob.
Fl. & Ob.

cresc.
cresc.
Viol.
marcato
Ped.
Clar.

Viol.
Ob.
dim.
sempre dim.
Clar.
p
pp
Viol.
Ped.
pp
Viola.
Ob & Clar.
f
Trombe.
Fl. & Ob.

Wood wind.
mf
p
p Strings
cresc.
cresc.
p
cresc.
p
Cor.
p
Ped.
Tromba.
p
cresc. molto

TUTTI.
con fuoco
cresc. molto
ff
Ped.
sempre con fuoco
con fuoco

fff
Ped.
Ped.
Ped

Act I.

Nº 1. INTRODUCTION & SONG.– (Phœbe.)

PHŒBE.
1. When
p
maid_en loves, she sits and sighs, She wanders to and fro; Un _ bid_den tear - drops
fill her eyes, And to all ques_tions she re_plies, With a sad "heigh - ho!"
meno mosso
'Tis but a lit_tle word— "heigh_ho!"

a tempo
So soft, 'tis scarcely heard— "heigh-ho!" An i-dle breath— Yet
life and-death May hang up-on a maid's "heigh-ho!"
C
An i-dle breath— Yet life and death May hang up-on a maid's "heigh-ho!"
f

2. When maid-en loves, she mopes a-part, As owl mopes on a
p
tree; Al-though she keen-ly feels the smart, She can-not tell what ails her heart, With its
sad "Ah me!"
meno mosso
'Tis but a fool-ish sigh- "Ah me!" Born but to droop and die- "Ah me!"

a tempo
Yet all the sense Of e - lo - quence Lies hid-den in a maid's "Ah
me!" Yet all the sense Of e - lo-quence Lies hid-den
in a maid's "Ah me!" "Ah me!" "Ah me!"
Yet all the sense Of e - loquence Lies hid - - den in a maid's "Ah
me!"
f

No. 2. DOUBLE CHORUS.—(People and Yeomen, with Solo 2nd Yeoman)

Foe - men scar - ing, In their by - gone days of dar - ing! Ne'er a stran - ger
Foe - men scar - ing, In their by - gone days of dar - ing! Ne'er a stran - ger
There to dan - ger— Each was o'er the world a ran - ger: To the sto - ry
There to dan - ger— Each was o'er the world a ran - ger: To the sto - ry
A
Of our glo - ry Each a bold, a bold con - tri - bu - to - ry!
Of our glo - ry Each a bold, a bold con - tri - bu - to - ry!
f

YEOMEN.
TENORS.
In the autumn of our life, Here at rest in ample clover, We rejoice in telling over Our impetuous May and June.
BASSES.
In the autumn of our life, Here at rest in ample clover, We rejoice in telling over Our impetuous May and June.
B
In the evening of our day, With the sun of life declining,
In the evening of our day, With the sun of life declining, We re-

We re_call with_out re_pi_ning All the heat of by_gone noon,
_call with_out re_pi_ning All the heat of by_gone noon,
We re_call with_out re_pi_ning, All the heat, We re_
We re_call with_out re_pi_ning, All the heat, We re_
un poco rall.
_call, re_call All the heat of by_gone noon.
un poco rall.
_call, re_call All of by_gone noon.
un poco rall.
a tempo f

C SOLO. 2nd YEOMAN.
This the au - tumn of our life, This the eve - ning
of our day; Wea - ry we of bat - tle strife,
D
Wea - ry we of mor - - - - - tal fray. But our
p

year_ is not so spent, And our days_ are not so fa - ded,
But that we with one con-sent, Were our lov - ed land in-va-ded,
Still would face a for - eign foe, As in days of long a-go, Still would
face a for - eign foe, As in days of long a - go, As in
days of long a - go, As in days of long a -
colla voce
E
p

YEOMEN.
go. Still would face a for - eign foe, As in days of long a -
Still would face a for - eign foe, As in days of long a -
f a tempo
PEOPLE.
Tow - er war - ders, Un - der or - ders, Gal - lant pike - men, va - liant sword - ers!
Tow - er war - ders, Un - der or - ders, Gal - lant pike - men, va - liant sword - ers!
go.
go.
Brave in bear - ing, Foe - men scar - ing, In their by - gone days of dar - ing!
Brave in bear - ing, Foe - men scar - ing,

KICKS

F

Tow - er war - ders, Un - der or - ders, Gal - lant pike - men, va - liant sword - ers!

Tow - er war - ders, Un - der or - ders, Gal - lant pike - men, va - liant sword - ers!

YEOMEN.

TENORS. *sost.*

This the au - tumn of our life,

BASSES. *sost.*

This the au - tumn of our life,

STEPS

Brave in bear - ing, Foe - men scar - ing, In their by - gone days of dar - ing!

Brave in bear - ing, Foe - men scar - ing, In their by - gone days of dar - ing!

This the eve - ning of our day,

This the eve - ning of our day,

knee pops?

Ne'er a stran_ger There to dan _ ger— Each was o'er the world a ran _ ger:

Ne'er a stran_ger There to dan _ ger— Each was o'er the world a ran _ ger:

Wea - ry we___ of bat - tle strife______

Wea - ry we___ of bat - tle strife______

& swishy hands

To the sto _ ry Of our glo _ ry Each a bold, a bold con _ tri _ bu _

To the sto _ ry Of our glo _ ry Each a bold, a bold con _ tri _ bu _

Wea _ - ry___ we___ of___ mor - - - - - - - tal

Wea _ - ry___ we___ of___ mor - - - - - - - tal

G

-to - ry! To the sto - ry Of our glo - ry Each a bold con - tri - bu -

-to - ry! To the sto - ry Of our glo - ry Each a bold con - tri - bu -

fray. This the au - - - - tumn of our life,___

fray. This the au - tumn of_ our life, This the eve - ning of_ our

f

-to - ry! Each a bold con - tri - bu - to - ry!

-to - ry! Each a bold con - tri - bu - to - ry!

— This the eve - ning of our day.

day, This the eve - ning of our day.

No. 3. SONG with CHORUS.– (Dame Carruthers and Yeomen.)

Allegro moderato e maestoso.
PIANO.
DAME CARRUTHERS.
1. When our gal_lant Normanfoes Made our mer_ry landtheirown, And the Sax_onsfrom the Con_quer_or were fly - ing, At his bid_ding it a_rose, In its pan - o_ply of stone, A sen - ti_nel un_liv - ing and un - dy - ing. In -
2. With - in its wall of rock The flow_er of the brave Have perishedwith a con_stan_cy un - sha - ken. From the dun_geon to the block, From the scaf_fold to the grave, Is a jour_ney ma - ny gal - lant hearts have ta - ken. And the

-sen-si-ble, I trow, As a sen-ti-nel should be, Tho' a queen to save her head should come a-
wick-ed flames may hiss Round the he-roes who have fought For conscience and for home in all its
-su-ing; There's a le-gend on its brow That is e-lo-quent to me, And it
beau-ty; But the grim old for-ta-lice Takes lit-tle heed of aught That
tells of du-ty done and du-ty do-ing,
comes not in the mea-sure of its du-ty.
p
p
"The screw may twist and the rack may turn, And

men may bleed and men may burn, O'er Lon - don town and its
gold - en hoard I keep my si - lent watch and ward!"
TENORS & BASSES. p
The
O'er Lon-don town and all its hoard,
cresc.
screw may twist and the rack may turn, And men may bleed and
p
cresc.

O'er London town and all its hoard
men may burn, O'er Lon - don town and its gold - en hoard I
I keep my si - - lent, si - - - lent watch and ward!
keep my si - - lent watch and ward!
1.
2.
rall.
si - - lent watch and ward!
watch and ward!
f
mf
p

Nº 4. TRIO.—(Phœbe, Leonard and Meryll.)

hearts that quail The hands that shrink the cheeks that pale In hours
cresc.
f
No, ours are not the hearts that
of need! No, ours are not the hearts that
No, ours are not the hearts that
quail, The hands that shrink, the cheeks that pale, The hands that
quail, The hands that shrink, the cheeks that pale, The hands that
quail, The hands that shrink, the checks that pale, that
cresc.

D
shrink,— the cheeks that pale In hours— of need!
shrink,— the cheeks that pale In hours— of need!
pale,— the cheeks that pale In hours— of need!
sf
p
p
MERYLL.
The
air I breathe to him I owe: My life is his— I count it naught!
dim.

PHŒBE.
C
That life is his— so count it naught!
LEONARD.
That life is his— so count it naught!
MERYLL.
And shall I reck - on risks I
p
run When ser - vi - ces are to be done To save the life of
such - an one?
Un - wor - thy thought! Un - wor -
Ped
Ped

D
PHŒBE & LEONARD.
And shall we reck - on risks we run — To save
- thy thought!
Ped.
the life of such an one? Un - wor - thy thought!
MERYLL.
Un - wor - thy thought!
Un - wor - thy thought!
E
Un - wor - thy thought!

PHOEBE.
We may suc - ceed— who can fore - tell? May heaven help our hope—
LEONARD.
We may suc - ceed— who can fore - tell? May heaven help our hope—
MERYLL.
We may suc - ceed— who can fore - tell? May heaven help our hope—
May heaven help our hope—
May heaven help our hope—
May heaven help our hope—
fare - - - - - well!
fare - - - - - well!
fare - - - - - well!

May
heaven
May
heaven
May
heaven
help
our
hope
dim.
Ped.
help
our
hope
fare
well!
help
our
hope
fare
well!
help
our
hope
fare
well!
p

No. 5. BALLAD (Fairfax.)

kind of plaint have I, Who per - ish in Ju - ly, Who per - ish
un poco rit.
a tempo
in Ju - ly! I might have had to die, Per -
colla voce
- chance, in June! I might have had to die, Per - chance, in
p
June!
f
p

2. Is life a thorn? Then count it not a whit! Nay,
count it not a whit! Man is well done___ with it;
Soon___ as he's born He should all means es_say To put the
plague a - way; And I, war - worn, Poor
Ped.
Ped.
Ped.

rall. un poco
cap - tured fu - gi - tive, My life most glad - ly give- I
colla voce
a tempo
might have had to live An - o - ther morn! I
might have had to live, to live An - o - ther morn!
colla voce
p
f

Nº 6. CHORUS:—(Entrance of Crowd, Elsie and Point.)

unis.
Come fool, fol-li-fy! If you va-pour va-pid-ly, Ri-ver run-neth ra-pid-ly,
Come fool, fol-li-fy! If you va-pour va-pid-ly, Ri-ver run-neth ra-pid-ly,
In-to it we-fling Bird who does-n't-sing! Give us an ex-per-i-ment
throw cock crow
In-to it we-fling Bird who does-n't-sing! Give us an ex-per-i-ment
In the art of mer-ri-ment; In-to it we-throw Cock who does-n't-crow.
In the art of mer-ri-ment; In-to it we-throw Cock who does-n't-crow.

B
Banish your ti-mid-i-ty,
And with all ra-pid-i-ty
unis.
Give us quip and quid-di-ty-
Banish your ti-mid-i-ty,
And with all ra-pid-i-ty
unis.
Give us quip and quid-di-ty-
Wil-ly-nil-ly, O!
Riv-er none can mol-li-fy;-
In-to it we throw
Wil-ly-nil-ly, O!
Riv-er none can mol-li-fy;-
In-to it we throw
Fool who does-n't fol-li-fy,
Cock who does-n't crow!
Ban-ish your ti-mid-i-ty,
Fool who does-n't fol-li-fy,
Cock who does-n't crow!
Ban-ish your ti-mid-i-ty,

And with all ra-pid-i-ty
Give us quip and quid-di-ty-
Wil-ly-nil-ly, O!
And with all ra-pid-i-ty
Give us quip and quid-di-ty-
Wil-ly-nil-ly, O!
sf
Dialogue through.
pp

No 7. DUET.– (Elsie and Point.)

soul was sad, and whose glance was glum, Who sipped no sup, and who craved no crumb, As he
sighed for the love of a la - dye, Heigh - dy! Heigh - dy! Mis-e - ry me,
pp
lack-a - day - dee! He sipped no sup, and he craved no crumb, As he sighed for the love of a
ELSIE.
la - dye! 2. I have a song to sing, O!

POINT.
ELSIE.
What is your song, O?
It is sung with the ring Of the songs maids sing Who
love with a love life - long, O! It's the song of a mer-ry-maid, peer-ly proud, Who lov'd a lord, and who
laugh'd a - loud At the moan of the mer-ry-man, mop-ing mum, Whose soul was sad, and whose
glance was glum, Who sipped no sup, and who craved no crumb, As he sighed for the love of a

la - dye! Heigh - dy! heigh - dy! Mis - e - ry me, lack - a - day - dee! He
pp
Ped.
sipped no sup, and he craved no crumb, As he sighed for the love of a la - dye!
Ped.
Ped.
Ped.
POINT.
ELSIE.
POINT.
3. I have a song to sing, O! Sing me your song! O! It is
sung to the knell Of a church - yard bell, And a dole - ful dirge ding dong, O! It's a
Ped.

song of a pop-in-jay, brave-ly born, Who turned up his no-ble nose with scorn At the
hum-ble mer-ry-maid, peer-ly proud, Who lov'd a lord, and who laugh'd a-loud At the
moan of the mer-ry-man, mop-ing mum, Whose soul was sad, and whose glance was glum, Who
sipped no sup, and who craved no crumb, As he sighed for the love of a la-dye! Heigh-dy!

Heigh - dy! mis-e-ry me, lack-a-day-dee! He sipped no sup, and he craved no crumb, As he
sighed for the love of a la - dye
ELSIE.
4. I have a song to sing, O!
POINT.
Sing me your song O!
ELSIE.
It is sung with a sigh And a tear in the eye, For it
tells of a right-ed wrong, O! It's a song of the mer-ry-maid, once so gay, Who
Ped.
Ped.

turned on her heel and tripped a-way From the pea-cock popin-jay, brave-ly born Who turned up his no-ble
nose with scorn At the hum-ble heart that he did not prize; So she begged on her knees, with
down-cast eyes, For the love of the mer-ry-man, mop-ing mum, Whose soul was sad and whose
glance was glum, Who sipped no sup, and who craved no crumb, As he sighed for the love of a la - dye!
Ped.

BOTH
Heigh - dy! Heigh - dy! Mis-e-ry me, lack-a-day-dee! His pains were o'er, and he
1st SOPRANOS
Heigh - dy! Heigh - dy! Mis-e-ry me, lack-a-day-dee! His pains were o'er, and he
p 2nd SOPRANOS
cresc.
Oo
TENORS & BASSES
p
cresc.
Oo
cresc.
molto
Ped.
sighed no more, For he lived in the love of a la - dye! Heigh - dy! Heigh - dy!
f
sighed no more, For he lived in the love of a la - dye! Heigh - dy! Heigh - dy!
f
Ah!
f
Ah!
f
Ped.

cresc.
Mis - e - ry me, lack-a - day - dee! His pains were o'er, and he sighed no more, For he
cresc.
Mis - e - ry me, lack-a - day - dee! His pains were o'er, and he sighed no more, For he
cresc.
cresc.
cresc.
lived in the love of a la - dye!
lived in the love of a la - dye!
ff
HEY!

No. 8. TRIO.—(Elsie, Point, and Lieutenant.)

truth the po - ets tell, Most bride - grooms, ere they
mar - ry, lose Both head and heart as well!
ELSIE.
A
strange pro - po - sal you re - veal, It al - most makes my sen - ses
reel. A - las! I'm ve - ry poor in - deed, And
such a sum I sore - ly need. My mo - ther, sir, is

like to die, This mo-ney life may bring, Bear
this in mind, I pray, if I Con-sent to do this
thing! Tho' as a gen'ral rule of life I don't al-low my prom-ised wife, My
POINT.
love-ly bride that is to be, To mar-ry a-ny-one but me, Yet

if the fee is prompt - ly paid, And he, in well earn'd grave,
With - in the hour is du - ly laid, Ob - jec - tion I will
E
waive! Yes, ob - jec - tion I will waive!
ELSIE.
Temp-ta - tion, oh, temp - ta - tion, Were we, I pray, in - tend-ed To shun, what-e'er our
POINT.
Temp-ta - tion, oh, temp - ta - tion, Were we, I pray, in - tend-ed To shun, what-e'er our
LIEUT.
Temp-ta - tion, oh, temp - ta - tion, Were we, I pray, in - tend-ed To shun, what-e'er our
p

sta - tion, Your fas - ci - na - tions splen - did; Or fall, when - e'er we view you,
sta - tion, Your fas - ci - na - tions splen - did; Or fall, when - e'er we view you,
sta - tion, Your fas - ci - na - tions splen - did; Or fall, when - e'er we view you,
cresc.
Head o-ver heels in - to you! Head o-ver heels, Head o-ver heels, Head o-ver heels in -
Head o-ver heels in - to you! Head o-ver heels, Head o-ver heels, Head o-ver heels in -
Head o-ver heels in - to you! Head o-ver heels, Head o-ver heels, Head o-ver heels in -
- to you! Oh, temp - ta - tion,
- to you! Head o-ver heels, Head o-ver heels, Head o-ver heels, Head o-ver
- to you! Head o-ver heels, Head o-ver heels, Head o-ver heels, Right in - to you!
f
sf
8

Oh. temp-
Head o-ver heels, Head o-ver heels, Head o-ver heels,
Head o-ver heels, Head o-ver heels, Head o-ver heels,
-ta - tion, Oh, temp - - -
Head o-ver heels, Head o-ver heels, Head o-ver heels, Head o-ver
Head o-ver heels, Head o-ver heels, Head o-ver heels, Head o-ver heels, Head
-ta - - - tion,
heels, Head o - ver heels, Head o-ver heels, Head o-ver heels, Head o-ver
o - ver heels, Head o - ver heels, Head o-ver heels, Head o-ver heels,

Oh, temp - - ta - - - tion

heels, Head o-ver heels, Head o-ver heels, Head o - ver heels, Head o-ver heels!

Head o-ver heels, Head o-ver heels, Head o-ver heels, Head o-ver, o-ver heels!

Più lento

Temp - ta - tion, oh, temp - ta - tion!

Temp - ta - tion, oh, temp - ta - tion!

Temp - ta - tion, oh, temp - ta - tion!

Più lento

No. 9. RECIT & SONG.-(Point.)

peer. At peer or prince — at prince or peer, I
aim my shaft and know no fear!
rall.
Allegretto non troppo vivace.
1. I've wis_dom from the East and from the West, That's
set a braggart quailing with a quip, The
subject to no ac_a_dem_ic rule; You may find it in the jeer_ing of a
up-start I can with_er with a whim, He may wear a mer_ry laugh up_on his
jest, Or dis_til it from the fol_ly of a fool. I can
lip, But his laugh_ter has an ec_ho that is grim! When they're
p

teach you with a quip; if I've a mind; I can trick you in - to learn - ing with a
of - fer'd to the world in mer - ry guise, Un - pleasant truths are swallowed with a
laugh; Oh win - now all my fol - ly, fol - ly, fol - ly, and you'll find A
will— For he who'd make his fel - low, fel - low, fel - low-creatures wise Should
grain or two of truth a - mong the chaff! Oh win - now all my fol - ly, fol - ly, fol - ly, and you'll find A
al - ways gild the phil - o - soph - ic pill! For he who'd make his fel - low, fel - low, fel - low-creatures wise Should
grain or two of truth a - mong the chaff!
al - ways gild the phil - o - sop - ic pill!
1.
2.
2. I can
sf
sf
f
p

Nº 10. RECIT. and SONG.–(Elsie.)

Moderato.
VOICE.
PIANO.
RECIT.
'Tis
p
done! I am a bride! Oh, lit-tle ring, That bear-est in thy
a tempo
p a tempo
cir-clet all the glad-ness That lov-ers hope for, and that po-ets
sing, What bringest thou to me but gold and sad-ness?

A bridegroom all un_known, save in this wise, To_day he dies! To-day, a_las, he
Allegro un poco agitato.
dies! Though tear and long-drawn sigh
p
Ill fit a bride,___ No sad_der wife than I The
whole world wide! Ah me! Ah

me!
Yet maids there be Who would con_sent to
lose The ve - ry rose of youth, The flow'r of
life, To be, in hon - est truth, A wed - ded wife,
No mat - ter whose! No mat_ter whose!

Ah me, what pro - fit we, O maids that sigh, Though
Ped. * Ped. * Ped. * Ped. * Ped. * Ped. *
poco rall.
gold, tho' gold should live, If wed - ded love must
cresc.
colla voce
f
mp
Ped. *
die?
a tempo
f
p
Ped. *
Ere half an hour has rung, A wi - dow I!
Ped. *

Ah heaven, he is too young, Too brave to die! Ah
me! Ah me! Yet
wives there be So wea - ry worn, I trow, That they would scarce complain,
So that they could In half an hour at - tain To wi - dow - hood,

No mat - ter how!
No mat-ter how!
O wea - ry wives,
Who wi - dow-hood would win,
Re - joice
re - joice, - that ye - have time - To wea - ry in!
poco rall.
cresc.
colla voce
f
mp
p

O wea - ry
wives, Who wi - dow - hood would win, Re - joice,
cresc.
f
Ossia.
- joice, O wea - ry, wea - ry wives, re -
brill.
re - joice, re - joice, O wea - ry, wea - ry wives, re -
sf
sf
sf
- joice!
- joice!
ff

No 11. SONG.— (Phoebe.)

I thy bride!
This heart of mine Would
be one heart with thine, And in that shrine Our hap_pi_ness would dwell—
Were
I thy bride!
And all day long Our
lives should be a song: No grief, no wrong Should make my heart re_bel—
Were

I thy bride! The sil - v'ry flute, The
me - lan - cho - ly lute, Were night owl's hoot To my low - whispered coo— Were
I thy bride! The sky - lark's trill Were
but dis - cord - ance shrill To the soft thrill Of woo - ing as I'd woo—
cresc.
Were I thy bride The
dim.
p

ro - se's sigh Were as a car-rion's cry To lul-la
-by Such as I'd sing to thee, Were I thy
bride! A fea - ther's press Were
lead-en hea-vi-ness To my car-ess. But then, of course, you see I'm
not thy bride!
pp

Nº 12. FINALE.—ACT I.

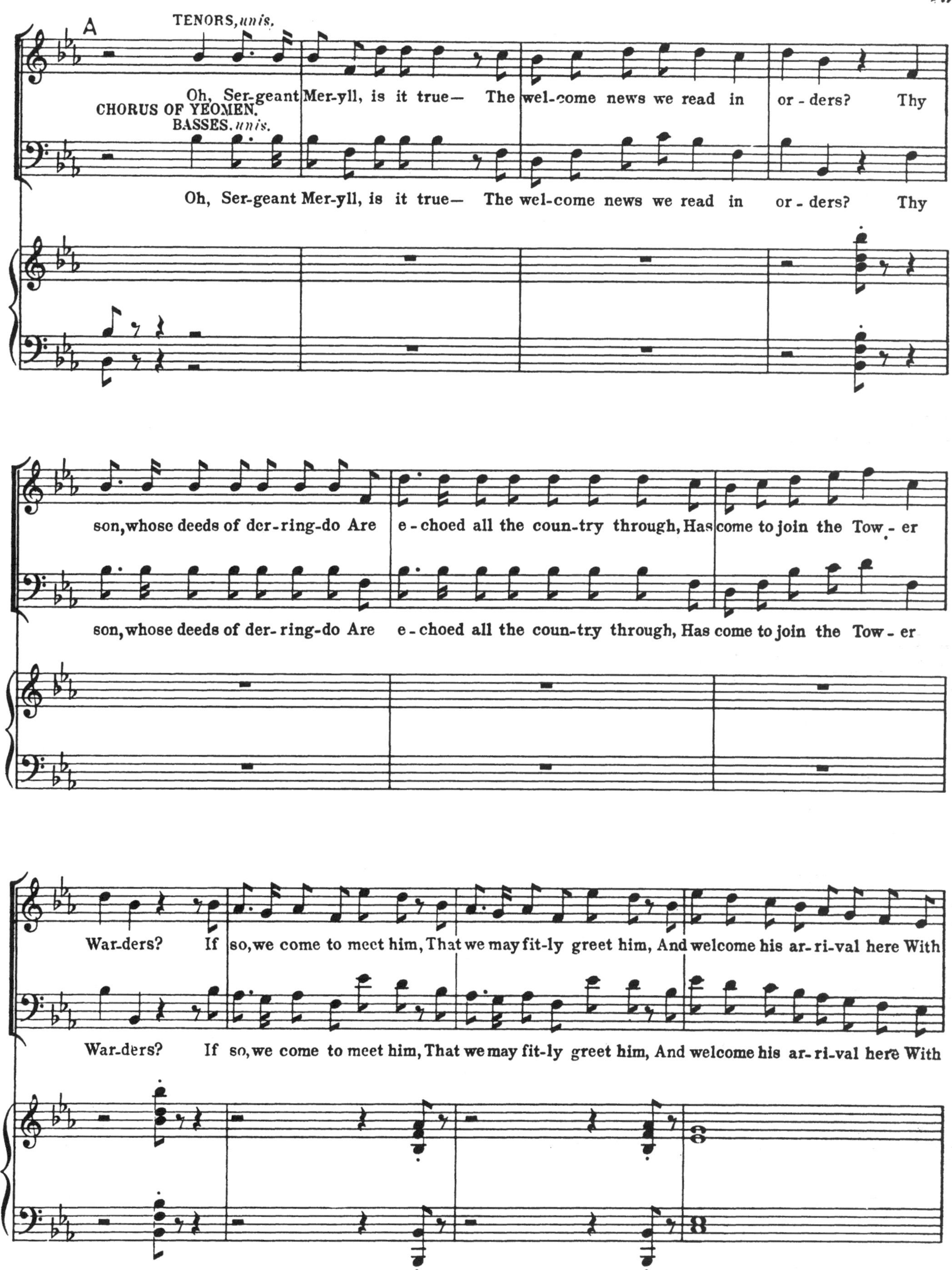
A
TENORS, unis.
Oh, Ser-geant Mer-yll, is it true— The wel-come news we read in or-ders? Thy
CHORUS OF YEOMEN.
BASSES. unis.
Oh, Ser-geant Mer-yll, is it true— The wel-come news we read in or-ders? Thy
son, whose deeds of der-ring-do Are e-choed all the coun-try through, Has come to join the Tow-er
son, whose deeds of der-ring-do Are e-choed all the coun-try through, Has come to join the Tow-er
War-ders? If so, we come to meet him, That we may fit-ly greet him, And welcome his ar-ri-val here With
War-ders? If so, we come to meet him, That we may fit-ly greet him, And welcome his ar-ri-val here With

shout on shout and cheer on cheer, Hur-rah! Hur-rah! Hur-rah!
shout on shout and cheer on cheer, Hur-rah! Hur-rah! Hur-rah!
dim.
mf
B
MERYLL.
Ye Tow - er War-ders, nursed in war's a-larms,
p
Suck-led on gun - pow-der and wean'd on glo - ry, Be-
-hold my son, whose all - sub - du - ing arms

Have form'd the theme of ma-ny a song and sto - ry! For-give his a-ged fa-ther's
pride; nor jeer His a-ged fa-ther's sym-pa-the-tic tear!
cresc.
f TENORS.
Leo - nard Mer - yll! Leo - nard Mer - yll! Daunt - less he in
f BASSES.
Leo - nard Mer - yll! Leo - nard Mer - yll! Daunt - less he in
ff
time of pe - ril! Man of pow - er, Knight-hood's flow - er,
time of pe - ril! Man of pow - er, Knight-hood's flow - er,

Wel-come to the grim old Tower: To the
Wel-come to the grim old Tower: To the
wel - come
Tow - er, wel - come thou!
Tow - er, wel - come thou!
D
FAIRFAX.
For-bear, my friends, and spare me this o - va-tion: I have small claim to such con-si-der-
-a-tion: The tales that of my prow-ess are nar - ra-ted Have been pro-di-gious-ly ex-ag-ger-

FAIRFAX.
-a - ted, pro - di - gious - ly ex - ag - ger - a - ted.
TENORS.
'Tis
BASSES.
'Tis
ev - er thus! Wher - ev - er va - lour true is found, True
ev - er thus! Wher - ev - er va - lour true is found, True
mo - des - ty will there a - bound.
mo - des - ty will there a - bound.
p
rall.

repeat

Andante allegretto.
1st YEOMAN. Didst thou not, oh, Leonard Mer_yll! Stan_dard lost in last cam_
_paign, Res_cue it at dead_ly pe_ril— Bear it safe_ly back a_gain?
Leo_nard
Leo_nard
E
2nd YEOMAN. Didst thou not, when pri_soner
Mer_yll, at his pe_ril, Bore it safe_ly back a _ gain!
Mer_yll, at his pe_ril, Bore it safe_ly back a _ gain!

ta_ken, And debarr'd from all es_cape, Face, with gal_lant heart un_sha_ken, Death in
most ap_pall_ing shape?
CHORUS OF MEN.
Leo_nard Mer_yll faced his pe_ril, Death in most ap_pall_ing
Leo_nard Mer_yll faced his pe_ril, Death in most ap_pall_ing
FAIRFAX.
Tru_ly I was to be pit_ied, Hav_ing but an hour to live,
shape!
shape!

I re - luc - tant - ly sub - mit - ted, I had no al - ter - na -
rall.
F
- tive! Oh! the tales that are nar - ra - ted Of my deeds of der - ring -
p
do, Have been much ex - ag - ger - a - ted, Ve - ry much ex - ag - ger -
a - ted, Scarce a word of them is true! Scarce a word of - them is

true!
f TENORS.
They are not ex_ag_ger_a_ted, Not at all ex_ag_ger_a_ted, Could not be ex_ag_ger_
f BASSES.
They are not ex_ag_ger_a_ted, Not at all ex_ag_ger_a_ted, Could not be ex_ag_ger_
più f
FAIRFAX.
Scarce a word of them is true!
_a_ted, Ev_'ry word of them is true!
_a_ted, Ev_'ry word of them is true!
f
RECIT. PHŒBE.
Leo_nard!
Allegro.
sempre f
RECIT.

FAIRFAX.
I beg your par - don?
PHOEBE.
Don't you know me?
a tempo
I'm lit-tle Phoe-be! Phoebe?
FAIRFAX.
Is this Phoebe?
G
What, lit-tle
p
Phoe - be?
(Aside.)
Who the deuce may she be?
It can't be Phoe - be, sure - ly?
WILFRED.
Yes, 'tis Phoe - be—

Your sis - ter Phœ - be! Your own lit - tle
sis - ter!
CHORUS OF MEN.
Aye, he speaks the truth; 'Tis
Aye, he speaks the truth; 'Tis
PHŒBE.
Oh, my
FAIRFAX.
Sis - ter Phœ - be!
Phoe - be!
Phoe - be!
Ped.
Ped.

H
bro - ther!
So
Why, how you've grown! I did not re-cog-nize you!
sempre p
ma - ny years!
Oh, my bro - ther!
Oh, my
sis - ter!
Oh, bro - ther!
Oh, bro - ther!
Oh, sis - ter!
Oh, sis - ter!
f

WILFRED.
Aye, hug him, girl! There are
three thou mayst hug— Thy fa_ther and thy bro_ther and— my_self.
FAIRFAX.
Thy_
_self, for_sooth? And who art thou thy_self?
p
WILFRED.
Good sir, we are be_troth'd,
PHOEBE.
Or more or
p
f
p

WILFRED.
less—
But ra_ther less than more.
To thy fond care I
Moderato.
p
RECIT.
do commend thy sis _ ter.
Be to her An
e_ver-watchful guardian— ea _ gle-eyed!
And when she feels (as some_times she does feel)
K a tempo moderato
Disposed to in_discrimin_ate ca _ ress,
Be thou at hand to take those favours from her.
CHORUS of MEN.
Be
Be
a tempo moderato

PHOEBE. tenderly.
Yes, yes, Be thou at hand to take those favours from me.
thou at hand to take those favours from her.
thou at hand to take those favours from her.
p
Allegro non troppo.
1st Verse WILFRED. To thy fra - ter - nal care Thy sis - ter I com - mend;
2nd Verse PHOEBE. a - mia - ble I've grown, So in - no-cent as well,
From ev - 'ry lurk - ing snare Thy love - ly charge de - fend:
That if I'm left a - lone The con - se-quen - ces fell No

And to a-chieve this end, Oh! grant, I pray, this boon— Oh
mor - tal can fore - tell, So grant, I pray, this boon— Oh
grant this boon—
grant this boon—
She shall not quit thy sight
I shall not quit thy sight
From
morn to af-ter-noon— From af-ter-noon to night— From seven o'clock to two— From
two to e-ven-tide— From dim twilight to 'leven at night, From dim twilight to 'leven at night
She
I
cresc.

CHORUS of MEN.
shall not quit thy side!
From morn to af - ter - noon — From
From morn to af - ter - noon — From
af - ter-noon to 'leven at night She shall not quit thy side!
af - ter-noon to 'leven at night She shall not quit thy side!
2nd Verse. PHŒBE. So
2. FAIRFAX.
With bro - ther-ly read - i - ness, For my fair sis -

-ter's sake, At once I an - swer
"Yes" That task I un - - der - - take
M
My word I ne-ver break I free-ly grant that boon, And
rall.
(Tenderly) sostenuto
(Kiss.)
(Kiss.)
I'll re-peat my plight From morn to af-ter-noon From af-ter-noon to night From
pp rall.
p un poco più lento

(Kiss)
(Kiss) Animato.
sev'n o-clock to two— From two to eve-ning meal— From dim twi-light to 'leven at night, From
tr
dim twi-light to 'leven at night, That com - pact I will seal.
CHORUS OF MEN.
f TENORS.
From morn to
f BASSES.
From morn to
cresc.
ff
af - ter-noon, From af - ter-noon to 'leven at night He free - ly grants that
af - ter-noon, From af - ter-noon to 'leven at night He free - ly grants that

Andante.
boon!
boon!
Andante.
pp
N
p

1st & 2nd SOPRANOS.
The pri-s'ner comes to meet his doom; The
TENORS & BASSES.
The pri-s'ner comes to meet his doom; The
block, the heads-man, and the tomb. The fun-'ral bell be-gins to
block, the heads-man, and the tomb. The fun-'ral bell be-gins to
toll; May Heav'n have mer-cy on his soul!
toll; May Heav'n have mer-cy on his soul!

mer - cy
May Heav'n have mer - - cy
May Heav'n have mer - - - cy
on his
on his soul!
ELSIE.
Oh,
on his soul!
P
Mer - cy, thou whose smile has shone So many a cap-tive heart up-
trem.
p
-on; Of all im-mured with - in these walls, To—

-day the ve - ry wor - thiest falls. Oh, Mer - cy, thou whose
SOPRANOS.
p
Oh, Mer - cy, thou whose
TENOR & BASSES.
p
Oh, Mer - cy, thou whose
smile has shone So ma-ny a cap-tive heart up - on; Of
smile has shone So many a cap-tive heart up - on; Of
smile has shone So many a cap-tive heart up - on; Of
all im - mured with - in these walls The wor - - -
cresc.
all im - mured with - in these walls, The
cresc.
all im - mured with - in these walls, The
cresc.
f

dim.
p
- - thiest,
wor - - - thiest
falls.
ve - ry
wor - - - thiest
falls.
Oh,
ve - ry
wor - - thiest
falls.
Oh,
tr
dim.
Oh, Mer - - cy.
Mer - - cy, oh, Mer - - cy.
Mer - - cy, oh, Mer - - cy.
Doppio movimento
Allegro agitato
FAIRFAX.
My lord! my lord! I
ff
fp

know not how to tell The news I bear! I and my
comrades sought the pris'ner's cell—
Q
He is not
cresc.
there!
CHORUS.
He is not there! They sought the pris - 'ner's
He is not there! They sought the pris - 'ner's
f
cell— he is not there!
R FAIRFAX 1st & 2nd YEOMEN.
As
cell— he is not there!
p

FAIRFAX & 1st YEOMAN.

escort for the prisoner We sought his cell, in duty bound; The double gratings open were, No prisoner at all we found! We

hunt_ed high, We hunt_ed here, The man we sought with anx - ious care Had

2nd YEOMAN.

We hunt_ed low, We hunt_ed there-The man we sought with anx - ious care Had

GIRLS.

Now,

van_ish'd in _ to emp_ty air! The man we sought with anxious care Had vanish'd in_to emp_ty air!

van_ish'd in . to emp_ty air! The man we sought with anxious care Had vanish'd in_to emp_ty air!

by my troth, the news is fair, The man has van_ish'd in - to
trow the
S
air. As es_cort for the pri_son_er They sought his cell, in du_ty bound; The
TENORS & BASSES.
As es_cort for the pri_son_er They sought his cell, in du_ty bound; The
FAIRFAX & 1st YEOMAN.
As es_cort for the pri_son_er We sought his cell, in du_ty bound; The
2nd YEOMAN.
As es_cort for the pri_son_er We sought his cell, in du_ty bound; The
dou_ble gratings op_en were, No pri_son_er at all they found, They hunt_ed high, They
dou_ble gratings op_en were, No pri_son_er at all they found, They hunt_ed low,
dou_ble gratings op_en were, No pri_son_er at all we found, We hunt_ed high, We
dou_ble gratings op_en were, No pri_son_er at all we found, We hunt_ed low,

hunt - ed here, The man they sought with an - xious care Had
They hunt - ed there— The man they sought with an - xious care Had
hunt - ed here, The man we sought with an - xious care Had
We hunt - ed there— The man we sought with an - xious care Had
van-ish'd in-to emp-ty air! The man they sought with anxious care Had vanish'd in-to emp-ty air!
van-ish'd in-to emp-ty air! The man they sought with anxious care Had vanish'd in-to emp-ty air!
van-ish'd in-to emp-ty air! The man we sought with anxious care Had vanish'd in-to emp-ty air!
van-ish'd in-to emp-ty air! The man we sought with anxious care Had vanish'd in-to emp-ty air!

T
LIEUTENANT.
(to WILFRED.)
As_tound_ing news! The pris_'ner fled.
Thy life shall for_feit be in_
_stead!
WILFRED.
My lord, I did not set him free,
I hate the man- my ri_val he!
U
LIEUT. (to WILFRED.)
Thy life shall for_feit be in_
MERYLL.
The pris_'ner gone- I'm all a_gape!
dolce

WILFRED.
-stead!
My lord,
Who could have help'd him to es - cape?
PHŒBE.
I did not set him free! In-deed I can't i - ma-gine who! I've no i - dea at all - have
DAME CARRUTHERS.
you? Of his es-cape no tra-ces lurk, Enchantment must have been at work!
ELSIE.
What have I
done! Oh, woe is me! I am his wife, and he is
PHŒBE & DAME CARRUTHERS.
In-deed I can't i-ma-gine who! I've no i-dea at all, have

POINT.
free! Oh! woe is you? Your an_guish sink! Oh, woe is
you?
me, I ra_ther think! Oh, woe is me, I rather think! Yes, woe is me, I rather think! Whate'er be_
_tide You are his bride, And I am left A_lone-be_reft! Yes, woe is me, I ra_ther think! Yes, woe is
cresc.
TUTTI. p
cresc. molto
Ah!
me, I rather think! Yes, woe is me, Yes, woe is me, Yes, woe is me, Yes, woe is me, I ra_ther
molto

Allegro con molto brio.
ff PHŒBE & DAME C.
All frenzied, frenzied with despair they rave, The grave is cheat-ed of its due. Who is, who
think. LIEUTENANT.
ff
(LIEUT.) All frenzied, frenzied with despair I rave, The grave is cheat_ed of its due. Who is, who
CHORUS. 1st & 2nd SOPS.
ff
All frenzied, frenzied with despair they rave, The grave is cheat_ed of its due. Who is, who
TENORS & BASSES. FAIRFAX with TENORS, WILFRED & MERYLL with BASSES.
ff
All frenzied, frenzied with despair, they rave, The grave is cheat_ed of its due. Who is, who
Allegro con molto brio.
ff
is the mis-be-got-ten knave Who hath con-triv'd this deed to do?
is the mis_be_got_ten knave Who hath con_triv'd this deed to do?
is the mis_be_got_ten knave Who hath con_triv'd this deed to do?
is the mis_be_got_ten knave Who hath con_triv'd this deed to do?
6
6

Let search, let search be made throughout the land, Or his— vin - dic-tive an - ger
Let search, let search be made throughout the land, Or my vin - dic - tive an - ger
Let search, let search be made throughout the land, Or his vin - dic - tive an - ger
Let search, let search be made throughout the land, Or his vin - dic - tive an - ger
sf
W
dread- A thou-sand marks, a thousand marks he'll hand Who brings him here, a-live or
(L.) dread- A thou-sand marks, a thousand marks I'll hand Who brings him here, a-live or
dread- A thou-sand marks, a thousand marks he'll hand Who brings him here, a-live or
dread- A thou-sand marks, a thousand marks he'll hand Who brings him here, a-live or
sf
sf
sf

dead, Who brings him here, a - live
(L.) dead, Who brings him here, a - live
dead, Who brings him here, a - live
dead, Who brings him here, a - live
sf
sf
Ped.
or dead! A thou - sand
(L.) or dead! A thou - sand, thou
or dead! A thou - sand
or dead! A thou - sand, thou
Ped.

marks, a thou - sand marks, a - live, a live or dead, a - live,
(L.) - - - - - sand marks, a - live, a - live or dead, a - live,
marks, a thou - - sand marks, a - live, a - live or dead, a - live,
- - - - - - sand marks, a - live, a - live or dead, a - live,
a - live or dead, Who brings him here, a - live, a - live
(L.) a - live or dead, Who brings him here, a - live, a - live
a - live or dead, Who brings him here, a - live, a - live
a - live or dead, Who brings him here, a - live, a - live

END OF ACT I.

Act II.

No 1. CHORUS. SOLO–(Dame Carruthers.)

1st & 2nd SOPRANOS.
Night has spread her pall once more, And the pris - - 'ner still is
free: O - - pen is his dun - geon door, Useless his
dun - - geon key!
1st SOP.
He has sha - - ken
off his yoke How, no mor - tal man can tell!

unis.
Shame on lout - ish jail - or-folk—
Shame on sleep - y sen - ti - nel!
SOLO. DAME CARRUTHERS.
Wardersare ye? Whomdo ye ward?
p
Warders are ye? Whomdo ye ward?
Bolt,bar, and key, Shackle and cord, Fetter and chain, Dungeon of stone, All are in vain—
Prisoner's flown!

Spite of ye all, he is free-he is free!
Whom do ye ward? Pretty warders are ye!
CHORUS. 1st & 2nd SOPRANOS.
Pretty warders are ye! Whom do ye ward?
unis.
Spite of ye all, he is free-he is free!
Whom do ye ward? Pretty warders are ye!
TENORS
Up and down, and in and out, Here and there, and round a-bout; Ev-'ry chamber, ev-'ry house,
BASSES.
Up and down, and in and out, Here and there, and round a-bout; Ev-'ry chamber, ev-'ry house,

Ev - 'ry chink that holds a mouse, Ev - 'ry crev - ice in the keep,
Ev - 'ry chink that holds a mouse, Ev - 'ry crev - ice in the keep,
Where a beetle black could creep, Ev'ry out-let, ev-'ry drain, Have we search'd, but all in vain, all in
Where a beetle black could creep, Ev'ry out-let, ev-'ry drain, Have we search'd, but all in vain, all in
CHORUS.
Warders are ye? Whom do ye ward? Warders are ye? Whom do ye
vain! Ev'ry house, ev'ry chink, ev'ry drain, Ev-'ry
vain! Ev'ry house, ev'ry chink, ev'ry drain, Ev-'ry

ward?
Night ___ has spread her
chamber, ev-'ry outlet Have we search'd, but all in
vain!
War-ders are
chamber, ev-'ry outlet Have we search'd, but all in
vain!
pall once more and _ the pris - 'ner still is free:
we. Whom do we ward? Whom do we ward?
Warders are we. Whom do we

O - - pen is his dun - geon door, Useless his dun - - geon
Warders are we. Spite of us all he is free, he is
ward? Whom do we ward? Whom do we ward? Spite of us all he is free, he is
O - - - - - pen is his
key! O - - pen is his
free! Pretty warders are we, he is free!
free! Spite of us all he is free, he is free!
cresc.

dun - - geon door, He is free! He is
Spite of us all he is free, he is free! Pretty warders are we, he is free! He is
Spite of us all he is free, he is free! Pretty warders are we, he is free! He is
free! Pretty warders are ye, he is free! He is free! Pretty warders are ye!
free! He is free! He is free! Pretty warders are we!
free! He is free! He is free! Pretty warders are we!

Nº 2. SONG:–(Point.)

Allegro comodo.
VOICE.
PIANO.
f
1. Oh! a pri_vate buf_foon is a
2. If you wish to suc_ceed as a
3. If your mas_ter is sur_ly, from
4. Comes a Bish_op, may_be, or a
5. Tho' your head it may rack with a
light-heart_ed loon, If you lis_ten to pop_u_lar ru_mour; From the
jes_ter, you'll need To con_sid_er each per_son's au_ri_cular: What is
get_ting up ear_ly (And tem_pers are short in the morn_ing;) An in_
sol_emn D. D.– Oh, be_ware of his an_ger pro_vok_ing! Bet_ter
bil_ious at_tack, And your sen_ses with tooth_ache you're los_ing, Don't be

morn to the night he's so joy - ous and bright, And he bub - bles with wit and good-
all right for B would quite scan - da - lize C (For C is so ve - ry par -
- op - por - tune joke is e - nough to pro - voke Him to give you, at once, a month's
not pull his hair—don't stick pins in his chair: He don't un - der - stand prac - ti - cal
mo - py and flat—they don't fine you for that, If you're pro - per - ly quaint and a -
- hu - mour! He's so quaint and so terse, both in prose and in verse; Yet though
- ti - cular); And D may be dull, and E's ve - ry thick skull Is as
warn - ing. Then if you re - frain, he is at you a - gain, For he
jok - ing. If the jests that you crack have an or - tho - dox smack, You may
- mus - ing! Tho' your wife ran a - way with a sol - dier that day, And took
peo - ple for - give his trans - gres - sion, There are one or two rules that all
emp - ty of brains as a la - dle; While F is F sharp, and will
likes to get va - lue for mo - ney; He'll ask then and there, with an
get a bland smile from these sa - ges; But should they by chance, be im -
with her your tri - fle of mo - ney; Bless your heart, they don't mind—they're ex -
fa - mi - ly fools Must ob - serve, if they love their pro - fes - sion! There are
cry with a carp, That he's known your best joke from his cra - dle! When your
in - so - lent stare, "If you know that you're paid to be fun - ny?" It
- port - ed from France, Half - a - crown is stopp'd out of your wa - ges! It's a
- ceed - ing - ly kind— They don't blame you— as long as you're fun - ny! It's a

one or two rules, Half - a - do _ zen may be, That all fa _ mi _ ly fools Of what
hu _ mour they flout, You can't let your _ self go; And it does put you out When a
adds to the task Of a mer _ ry - man's place, When your prin _ ci _ pal asks, With a
gen _ e _ ral rule, Tho' your zeal it may quench, If the fa _ mi _ ly fool Tells a
com _ fort to feel If your part _ ner should flit, Tho' you suf _ fer a deal, They don't
ev _ er de _ gree, Must ob _ serve, if they love their pro _
per _ son says, "Oh, I have known that old joke from my
scowl on his face, If you know that you're paid to be
joke that's too French, Half - a - crown is stopp'd out of his
mind it a bit- They don't blame you- so long as you're
1, 2, 3 & 4.
_ fes _ sion.
cra _ dle!"
fun _ ny?
wa _ ges!
5.
fun _ ny!
ff

Nº 3. DUET:—(Point and Wilfred.)

Allegro vivace.
PIANO.
f
POINT.
1. Here-up-on we're both a-greed, All that we two Do a-gree to We'll se-
2. In re-turn for my own part I am mak-ing Un-der-tak-ing, To in-
WILFRED.
1. Here-up-on we're both a-greed, All that we two Do a-gree to We'll se-
2. In re-turn for your own part You are mak-ing Un-der-tak-ing, To in-
p
-cure by sol-emn deed, To pre-vent all Er-ror men-tal. You on El-sie are to
-struct you in the art (Art a-maz-ing, Won-der rais-ing) Of a jes-ter, jest-ing
cure by sol-emn deed, To pre-vent all Er-ror men-tal.
-struct me in the art (Art a-maz-ing, Won-der rais-ing)

call With a sto - ry Grim and go - ry;
free. Proud po - si - tion- High am - bi - tion!
How this Fair - fax died, and all I de -
And a live - ly one I'll be, Wag - a -
- clare to You're to swear to!
- wag - ging, Ne - ver flag - ging,
I to swear to!
Wag - a - wag - ging,
I de - clare to,
ne - ver flag - ging,
I to swear to!
Wag - a - wag - ging,
I de -
ne - ver
I to swear to, You de - clare to, I to swear to!
ne - ver flag - ging, Wag - a - wag - ging, ne - ver flag - ging!
- clare to, I de - clare to You're to swear to, I de - clare to!
flag - ging, Wag - a - wag - ging, ne - ver flag - ging, Wag - a - wag - ging!

Tell a tale of cock and bull, Of con - vin - cing
Tell a tale of cock and bull, Of con - vin - cing
p
8
de-tail full! Tale tre - men - dous, Heav'n de - fend us!
de-tail full! Tale tre - men - dous, Heav'n de - fend us!
8
What a tale of cock and bull! bull! What a tale of
What a tale of cock and bull! bull!
1.
2.
f
p

cock, What a tale of cock, What a tale of cock and bull, cock and
What a tale of bull! What a tale of bull! What a tale of cock and bull, cock and
bull, cock and bull! Heav'n de_fend us! What a tale of cock and bull!
bull, cock and bull! Heav'n de_fend us! What a tale of cock and bull!
cresc.
ff

Nº 4. BALLAD.—(Fairfax.)

Andante con espress.
VOICE.
PIANO.
p
Free from his fet - ters grim—
Free to de - part;
Free both in life and limb—
In all but heart!
Bound to an un-known bride
For good and ill;
Ah, is not one so tied
A

pris - 'ner still, A pris - 'ner still? Ah, is not one so
dim.
p
tied A pris - 'ner still?
f
Free, yet in fet - ters held Till his last hour,
Gyves that no smith can weld, No rust de - vour!

Al - though a monarch's hand Had set him free,
Of all the cap-tive band The sad - - - - - dest
cresc.
he, The sad - - dest he! Of all the cap-tive band The
dim.
dim.
p
rall.
sad-dest, sad - dest he!
colla voce
f

Nº 5. QUARTET.—(Kate, Dame Carruthers, Fairfax, and Sergeant Meryll.)

Allegretto. Tempo di Gavotte.
KATE.
1. Strange ad-venture! Maid-en wed-ded To a groom she'd ne-ver seen! Groom a-bout to be be-
2. Strange ad-venture that we're troll-ing: Mod-est maid and gal-lant groom! While the fun-'ral bell is
D. CARRUTHERS.
1. Strange ad-venture! Maid-en wed-ded To a groom she'd ne-ver seen! Ne-ver, ne-ver, ne-ver, seen! Groom a-bout to be be-
2. Strange ad-venture that we're troll-ing: Mod-est maid and gal-lant groom! Gal-lant, gal-lant, gal-lant groom! While the fun-'ral bell is
FAIRFAX.
1. Strange ad-venture! Maid-en wed-ded To a groom she'd ne-ver seen! Ne-ver, ne-ver, ne-ver, seen! Groom a-bout to be be-
2. Strange ad-venture that we're troll-ing: Mod-est maid and gal-lant groom! Gal-lant, gal-lant, gal-lant groom! While the fun-'ral bell is
Sgt. MERYLL.
1. Strange ad-venture! Maid-en wed-ded To a groom she'd ne-ver seen! Groom a-bout to be be-
2. Strange ad-venture that we're troll-ing: Mod-est maid and gal-lant groom! While the fun-'ral bell is
Allegretto. Tempo di Gavotte.
PIANO.
f
p
dim.

dim.
p
-headed, In an- hour on Tow-er Green! Groom in dreary-y- dungeon
toll-ing, Toll-ing, toll-ing, Bim-a - boom! Mod-est maid-en will not
p.
p
-headed, In an hour on Tow-er Green! Tow-er, Tow-er, Tow-er Green! Groom in dreary-y dungeon
toll-ing, Toll-ing, toll-ing, Bim-a - boom! Bim-a, Bim-a, Bim-a - boom! Mod-est maid-en will not
p
p
-head-ed, In an hour on Tow-er Green! Tow-er, Tow-er, Tow-er Green! Groom in dreary-y dun-geon
toll-ing, Toll-ing, toll-ing, Bim-a - boom! Bim-a, Bim-a, Bim-a - boom! Mod-est maid-en will not
p
-head-ed, In an hour on Tow-er Green! Groom in dreary-y dun-geon
toll-ing, Toll-ing, toll-ing, Bim-a - boom! Mod-est maid-en will not
cresc.
f
dim.
ly-ing-Groom as good as dead, or dy-ing, For a pret-ty maid-en sigh-ing-Pret-ty maid of sev-en-
tar-ry; Though but six-teen year she car-ry, She must mar-ry, she must mar-ry-Though the al-tar be a
cresc.
f
dim.
ly-ing-Groom as good as dead, or dy-ing, For a pret-ty maid-en sigh-ing-Pret-ty maid of sev-en-
tar-ry; Though but six-teen year she car-ry, She must mar-ry, she must mar-ry-Though the al-tar be a
cresc.
f
dim.
ly-ing-Groom as good as dead, or dy-ing, For a pret-ty maid-en sigh-ing-Pret-ty maid of sev-en-
tar-ry; Though but six-teen year she car-ry, She must mar-ry, she must mar-ry-Though the al-tar be a
cresc.
f
dim.
ly-ing-Groom as good as dead, or dy-ing, For a pret-ty maid-en sigh-ing-Pret-ty maid of sev-en-
tar-ry; Though but six-teen year she car-ry, She must mar-ry, she must mar-ry-Though the al-tar be a

1.
2.
p
-teen! Sev-en- sev-en-sev-en-teen! tomb! Tow-er tomb!
tomb- Tow-er, Tow-er, Tow-er
-teen! Sev-en- sev-en-sev-en-teen! tomb! Tow-er tomb!
tomb- Tow-er, Tow-er, Tow-er
-teen! Sev-en- sev-en-sev-en-teen! tomb! Tow-er tomb!
tomb- Tow-er, Tow-er, Tow-er
-teen! Sev-en- sev-en-sev-en-teen! tomb! Tow-er tomb!
tomb- Tow-er, Tow-er, Tow-er
cresc.
Slower.
dim.
Tow-er tomb! Though the al-tar be a tomb! Tow-er, Tow-er, Tow-er tomb!
Tow-er tomb! Though the al-tar be a tomb! Tow-er, Tow-er, Tow-er tomb!
Tow-er tomb! Though the al-tar be a tomb! Tow-er, Tow-er, Tow-er tomb!
Tow-er tomb! Though the al-tar be a tomb! Tow-er, Tow-er, Tow-er tomb!
Slower.

No 6. SCENE.—(Elsie, Phœbe, Dame Carruthers, Fairfax, Wilfred, Point, Lieutenant, Sergeant Meryll, and Chorus.)

CHORUS.
TENORS.

Now what can that have been— a shot so late at night, E-

BASSES.

Now what can that have been— a shot so late at night, E-

-nough to cause af - fright! What can the por - tent mean?

-nough to cause af - fright! What can the por - tent mean?

TUTTI.
SOPRANOS.

Are foe-men in the land? Is Lon-don to be wreck'd? What are we to ex-pect? What

TENORS & BASSES.

Are foe-men in the land? Is Lon-don to be wreck'd?

sf *sf* *sf*

Ped. * Ped. * Ped. *

dan-ger is at hand? Let us un - der-stand What dan-ger is at
What are we to ex-pect? What dan-ger is at hand What dan-ger is at
sf
sf
RECIT.
LIEUT.
hand! Who fired that shot! At once the truth de-clare!
hand!
RECIT.
fp
POINT.
My lord 'twas he— to rash-ly judge for-
WILFRED.
My lord, 'twas I— to rash-ly judge for-bear!
f
mf

Allegro con brio.
- bear!
ff
p
POINT.
Or a spec - tre all ap - pal - ling—
WILFRED.
Like a ghost his vi - gil keep - ing—
I be -
pp
I should ra - ther call it crawLing—
He was crawling—
- held a fi - gure creeping—
He was creeping—
He was
Crawling!
He was crawling—
Crawling!
creeping, creeping—
He was creeping—
He was creeping, creeping—
Not a

moment's hes_i_ta_tion-I my_self up_on him flung, With a hur_ried ex_clam_a_tion To his
dra_per_ies I hung; Then we clos'd with one an_o_ther In a rough-and-tumble smother; Col_'nel
Fair_fax and no o_ther Was the man to whom I clung!
ELSIE with 1st SOPS.
PHŒBE & DAME C. with 2nd SOPS.
FAIRFAX with TENORS.
Col_'nel Fair_fax and no o_ther, Col_'nel
LIEUT. & MERYLL with BASSES.
Col_'nel Fair_fax and no o_ther, Col_'nel
Fair_fax and no o_ther, Col_'nel Fair_fax and no o_ther Was the man to whom he clung!
Fair_fax and no o_ther, Col_'nel Fair_fax and no o_ther Was the man to whom he clung!

POINT.
It re - sem - bled more a struggle—
WILFRED.
Af - ter migh - ty tug and tus - sle—
He, by
p
pp
Or by some in - fer - nal juggle—
I should
dint of stronger muscle—
From my clutches quickly slid - ing—
ra - ther call it slip - ping—
Or es - cap - ing to the ship - ping—
With the view, no doubt, of hid - ing—
With a

I'd de - scribe it as a shiv - er—
gasp, and with a quiv - er—
Down he dived in - to the ri - ver, And, a -
- las, I can - not swim!
TUTTI.
CHORUS.
p
It's e - nough to make one shiv - er, With a gasp, and with a quiv - er, Down he
f
p
It's e - nough to make one shiv - er, With a gasp, and with a quiv - er, Down he
f
p
f
WILFRED.
In - ge -
dived in - to the ri - ver, It was ve - ry brave of him!
p
dived in - to the ri - ver, It was ve - ry brave of him!
p
p

POINT.
I should
- nu - i - ty is catching; With the view my king of pleasing, Ar - que - bus from sen - try snatching—
ra - ther call it seiz - ing—
With an ounce or two of lead I des - patch'd him thro' the head!
TUTTI.
CHORUS.
With an
With an
WILFRED.
I dis - charg'd it without winking, Lit - tle
ounce or two of lead He des - patch'd him thro' the head!
ounce or two of lead He des - patch'd him thro' the head!

POINT.
I should say a lump of lead.
time I lost in thinking, Like a stone I saw him sink_ing—
TUTTI.
CHORUS.
He dis_
He dis_
f
POINT.
I should
WILFRED.
Like a stone I saw him sinking—
_charg'd it with-out winking, Lit_tle time he lost in think_ing!
_charg'd it with-out winking, Lit_tle time he lost in think_ing!
say a lump of lead.
Like a hea_vy lump of lead.
Like a stone, my boy, I said—
Like a

Like a hea_vy lump of lead.
stone, my boy, I said— A_ny - how the man is dead. Whether
stone or lump of lead!
TUTTI.
CHORUS.
cresc.
A_ny - how the man is dead, And whether stone or lump of lead, Ar_que -
cresc.
A_ny - how the man is dead, And whether stone or lump of lead, Ar_que -
cresc.
f
_bus from sen_try seizing, With the view his king of pleasing, Ar_que - bus from sentry seiz_ing, With the
queen
_bus from sen_try seizing, With the view his king of pleasing, Ar_que - bus from sentry seiz_ing, With the

ff
view his king of pleasing, Wil_fred shot him thro' the head, And he's ve_ry, ve_ry dead! And it
ff
view his king of pleasing, Wil_fred shot him thro' the head, And he's ve_ry, ve_ry dead! And it
ff
sf
stringendo
mat_ters ve_ry lit_tle whether stone or lump of lead, It is ve_ry, ve_ry certain that he's
mat_ters ve_ry lit_tle whether stone or lump of lead, It is ve_ry, ve_ry certain that he's
stringendo
RECIT. LIEUT.
The riv_er must be dragged— No time be
ve_ry, ve_ry, dead!
ve_ry, ve_ry, dead!
ff
ff
fp RECIT.

lost, The bo - dy must be found, at a - ny cost. To this at -
a tempo
- tend with - out un - due de - lay; So set to work with what dis - patch ye
p a tempo animato
may!
TUTTI
CHORUS.
Yes, yes, we'll set to work with what dispatch we may!
Yes, yes, we'll set to work with what dispatch we may!
f
ff
Hail the va - liant fel - low who Did this
ff
Hail the va - liant fel - low who Did this
ff sf sf sf

deed_ of der_ring-do! Hon - ours wait on such an
deed of der_ring-do! Hon - ours wait on such an
sf
Ped. *
one; By my head, 'twas brave - - ly done, 'twas
one; By my head, 'twas brave - - ly done, 'twas
brave - - ly done! Now, by my head,'twas bravely done!
brave - - ly done! Now, by my head,'twas bravely done!
Ped.
*
Ped. *

No. 7. TRIO.—(Elsie, Phœbe, and Fairfax.)

Allegretto grazioso.
VOICE.
VOICE.
PIANO.
ELSIE. 2nd Verse.
If he's
FAIRFAX. 1st Verse.
A
f
psf
made the best use of his time, His twig he'll so care-ful-ly lime That
man who would woo a fair maid, Should 'pren-tice him-self to the trade, And
ev - e-ry bird Will come down at his word, What-ev - er its plu-mage or clime. He must
stu - dy all day, In me - tho-di-cal way, How to flat - ter, ca-jole, and per-suade He should

learn that the thrill of a touch May mean lit - tle, or no - thing, or much; It's an -
'pren - tice him - self at four - teen, And prac - tice from morn - ing to e'en; And
in - strument rare, To be han - dled with care, And ought to be treat - ed as such, ought
when he's of age, If he will, I'll en - gage, He may cap - ture the heart of a queen, the heart
to be treat - ed as such. It is pure - ly a mat - ter of skill, Which
PHŒBE.
It is pure - ly a mat - ter of skill, Which
of a queen! It is pure - ly a mat - ter of skill, Which

all may at-tain if they will— But ev-e-ry Jack, He must stu-dy the knack If he
all may at-tain if they will— But ev-e-ry Jack, He must stu-dy the knack If he
all may at-tain if they will— But ev-e-ry Jack, He must stu-dy the knack If he
cresc.
wants to make sure of his Jill! If he wants to make sure— of his Jill!
wants to make sure of his Jill! If he wants to make sure— of his Jill!
wants to make sure of his Jill! If he wants to make sure— of his Jill!
sf
1.
ELSIE
If he's
2.
PHOEBE.
Then a
p
f

glance may be tim - id or free, It will va - ry in might - y de-
p
-gree, From an im - pu-dent stare To a look of des - pair That no
maid with-out pi - ty can see; And a glance of des - pair is no
guide— It may have its ri - dic - u-lous side; It may

draw you a tear Or a box on the ear; You can nev - er be sure till you've
rall.
tried! Ne - ver be sure till you've tried!
rall.
a tempo
It is
It is
It is
colla voce
a tempo
pure - ly a mat - ter of skill, Which all may at - tain if they will. But
pure - ly a mat - ter of skill, Which all may at - tain if they will. But
pure - ly a mat - ter of skill, Which all may at - tain if they will. But

ev - e - ry Jack He must stu - dy the knack If he wants to make sure of his
ev - e - ry Jack He must stu - dy the knack If he wants to make sure of his
ev - e - ry Jack He must stu - dy the knack If he wants to make sure of his
Jill If he wants to make sure, to make sure of his Jill! sure of his Jill! If he
Jill If he wants to make sure, of his Jill, But ev - 'ry Jack, Must stu - dy the knack, But ev - 'ry Jack, Must stu - dy the knack If he
Jill If he wants to make sure, of his Jill, But ev - 'ry Jack, Must stu - dy the knack, But ev - 'ry Jack, Must stu - dy the knack If he

wants to make sure of his Jill! Yes, ev-e-ry Jack, Must
wants to make sure of his Jill! Yes, ev-e-ry Jack, Must
wants to make sure of his Jill! Yes, ev-e-ry Jack, Must
f
stu-dy the knack If he wants to make sure of his Jill!
stu-dy the knack If he wants to make sure of his Jill!
stu-dy the knack If he wants to make sure of his Jill!
tr
p
f

Nº 8. QUARTET.—(Elsie, Phœbe, Fairfax, & Point.)

happy days of do-ing! Oh, the sighing and the suing! When a woo-er goes a - woo-ing, Oh, the
happy days of do-ing! Oh, the sighing and the suing! When a woo-er goes a - woo-ing, Oh, the
happy days of do-ing! Oh, the sighing and the suing! When a woo-er goes a - woo-ing, Oh, the
- ing! Oh, the sighing and the suing! When a woo-er goes a - woo-ing, Oh, the
Ped. *
sweets that ne - ver cloy!
sweets that ne - ver cloy! When a brother leaves his sis-ter For an-
sweets that ne - ver cloy!
sweets that ne - ver cloy!
-oth-er, Sis-ter weeps. Tears that trickle, Tears that blis-ter-'Tis but mickle Sis - ter reaps! Tears that

ELSIE.
Oh, the
PHŒBE.
tric - - kle, Tears that blis - - ter—
Oh, the
FAIRFAX.
Oh, the
POINT.
Oh, the doing and un - do - -
doing and un - do_ing, Oh, the sighing and the su_ing, When a brother goes a - wooing, And a
doing and un - do_ing, Oh, the sighing and the su_ing, When a brother goes a - wooing, And a
doing and un - do_ing, Oh, the sighing and the su_ing, When a brother goes a - wooing, And a
- ing, Oh, the sighing and the su_ing, When a brother goes a - wooing, And a

D
sobbing sis - ter weeps!
sobbing sis - ter weeps!
sobbing sis - ter weeps!
sobbing sis - ter weeps! When a jes_ter Is out - witted, Feelings
fes_ter, Heart is lead! Food for fishes On_ly fit_ted, Jes_ter wishes He was
dead! Food for fishes On_ly fit_ted, Jes - ter wishes He was dead!

Oh, the doing and un - do-ing, Oh, the sighing and the suing, When a jes-ter goes a-
Oh, the doing and un - do-ing, Oh, the sighing and the suing, When a jes-ter goes a-
Oh, the doing and un - do-ing, Oh, the sighing and the suing, When a jes-ter goes a-
Oh, the doing and un - do-ing, Oh, the sighing and the suing, When a jes-ter goes a-
E
-wooing, And he wishes he was dead! Oh, the do-ing and un -
-wooing, And he wishes he was dead! Oh, the do-ing and un -
-wooing, And he wishes he was dead! Oh, the do-ing and un -
-wooing, And he wishes he was dead! Oh, the do-ing and un -

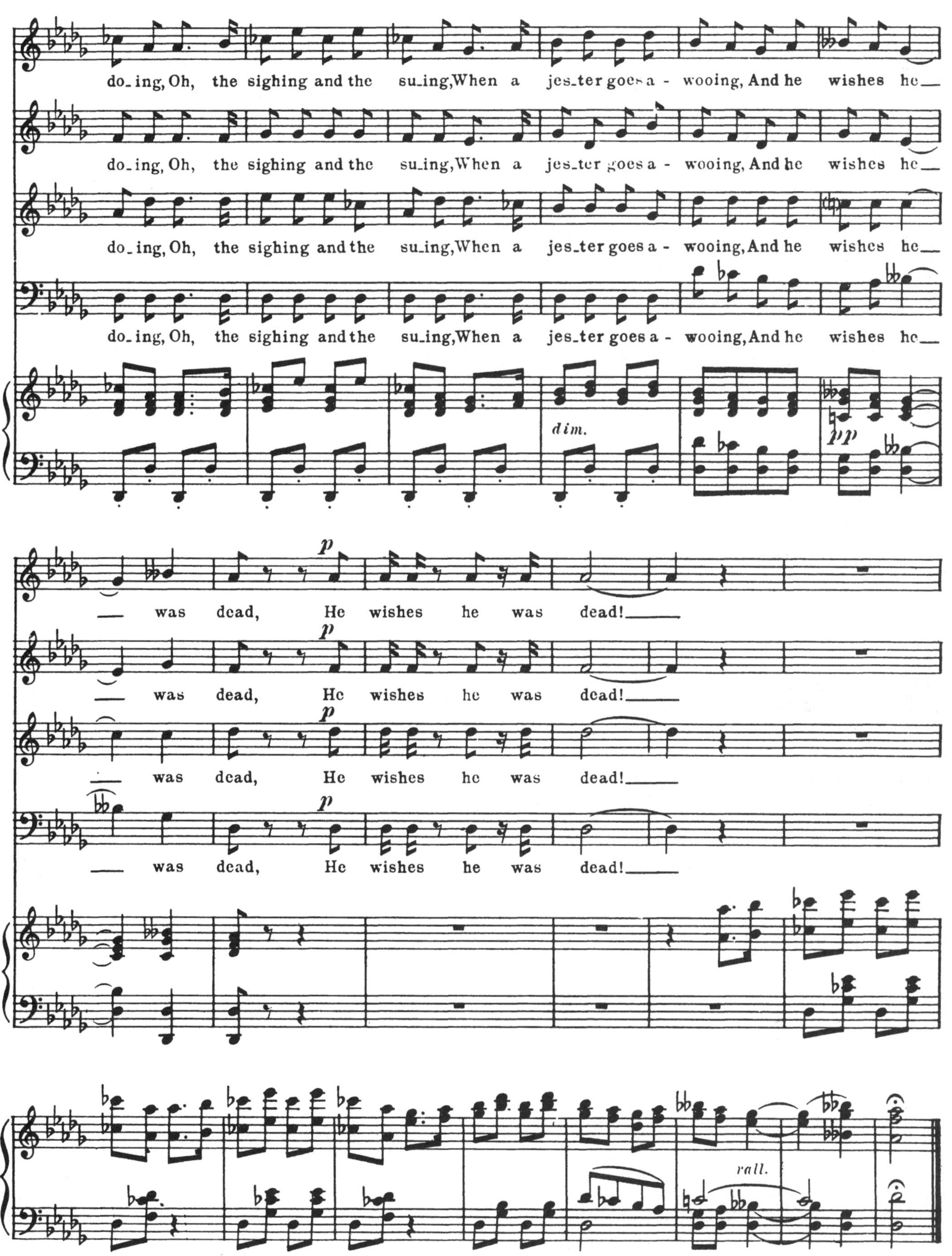
do_ing, Oh, the sighing and the su_ing, When a jes_ter goes a - wooing, And he wishes he
do_ing, Oh, the sighing and the su_ing, When a jes_ter goes a - wooing, And he wishes he
do_ing, Oh, the sighing and the su_ing, When a jes_ter goes a - wooing, And he wishes he
do_ing, Oh, the sighing and the su_ing, When a jes_ter goes a - wooing, And he wishes he
dim.
pp
p
was dead, He wishes he was dead!
p
was dead, He wishes he was dead!
p
was dead, He wishes he was dead!
p
was dead, He wishes he was dead!
rall.

Nº 9. DUET.—(Dame Carruthers and Sergeant Meryll.)

SERGEANT MERYLL.
Rap_ture, rap _ ture! Dole _ ful, dole _ ful! When hu_man_i _ ty, With its soul full
Of sat_an_i _ty, Court _ ing pri_vi_ty, Down de_cli_vi _ ty Seeks cap_ti_vi_ty!
Dole _ ful, dole _ ful! Court _ ing pri_vi_ty, Down de_cli_vi_ty Seeks cap_ti _ vi _ ty!
DAME CARRUTHERS.
Dole_ful, dole _ ful! Joy _ ful, joy _ ful! When vir_gin_i_ty Seeks, all coy _ ful,

Man's af-fin-i-ty; Fate all flow-er-y, Bright and bow-er-y Is her dow-er-y!
Joy-ful, joy-ful! Fate all flow-er-y, Bright and bow-er-y Is her dow-er-y,
SERGEANT MERYLL.
Joy-ful, joy-ful! Ghast-ly, ghast-ly! When man, sor-row-ful, First-ly, last-ly,
Of to-mor-row full, Af-ter tar-ry-ing, Yields to har-ry-ing—Goes a-mar-ry-ing,

DAME CARRUTHERS.
Joy - ful, joy - ful! Joy - ful, joy - ful!
Ghast - ly, ghast - ly! Ghast - ly, ghast - ly!
Joy - ful, joy - ful! Joy - ful, joy - ful, joy - ful!
Ghast - ly, ghast - ly! Ghast - ly, ghast - ly! Ghast - ly, ghast - ly, ghast - ly!
cresc.
f
Rap - ture, rap - ture! When love's vo - ta - ry, Flushed with cap - ture,
Dole - ful, dole - ful! When hu - man - i - ty, With its soul full
dim.
p

Seeks the no_ta_ry, Joy and jol_li_ty Then is pol_i_ty, Reigns fri_vol_i_ty!
Of sat_an_i_ty, Court_ing pri_vi_ty Down de_cli_vi_ty, Seeks cap_ti_vi_ty!
Rap_ture, rap_ture! Joy and jol_li_ty Then is po_li_ty; Reigns frivol_i_ty!
Dole_ful, dole_ful! Court_ing pri_vi_ty, Down de_cli_vi_ty, Seeks capti_vi_ty!
Rap_ture, rap_ture,
Rap_ture, rap_ture,
Dole_ful, dole_ful!
Dole_ful, dole_ful!

Rap - - ture, Rap - - - ture, rap - - ture, rap - - - - ture! Joy and jol-li-ty, Then is po-li-ty; Reigns fri-vol-i-ty! Rap-ture, rap - - - - - ture!
Dole - - ful, Dole - - - ful, dol - - ful, Dole - - - - ful! Court-ing pri-vi-ty, Down de-cli-vi-ty Seeks cap-ti-vi-ty! Dole-ful, dole - - - - - ful!
cresc.

No. 10. FINALE—ACT II. (Tutti.)

lot thou art will_ing_ly link - ing!
lot thou art will_ing_ly link - ing!
Flow_er of valour is he—
lov_ing as lov_ing can be!
Brightly thy summer is shin - ing
Brightly thy summer is shin - ing
Ped.
Brightly thy summer is shin - ing, Fair as the dawn, as the dawn of the
Brightly thy summer is shin - ing, Fair as the dawn, as the dawn of the

day; Take him, be_ true to him— Ten_der___ his_
day; Take him, be_ true to him— Ten_der___ his_
due to him— Honour him,__ honour him,__ love
due to him— Honour him,__ honour him,__ love
cresc.
mf
dimin.
TRIO. ELSIE.
mf
— and__ o_bey! 'Tis said that joy in full per_fec_tion Comes on_ly
PHŒBE.
mf
— and__ o_bey! 'Tis said that joy in full per_fec_tion Comes on_ly
DAME CARRUTHERS.
mf
'Tis said that joy in full per_fec_tion Comes on_ly
p

once_ to_ wo - man - kind— That, o _ ther times, on close in - spec _ tion, Some lurking
once_ to_ wo - man - kind— That, o _ ther times, on close in - spec _ tion, Some lurking
once_ to_ wo - man - kind— That, o _ ther times, on close in - spec _ tion, Some lurking
bit - ter we_ shall find. If this be so, and men say tru - ly, My
bit - ter_ we_ shall find. If this be so, and men say tru - ly, Her
bit - ter_ we_ shall find. If this be so, and men say tru - ly, Her
day of joy has bro_ken du - ly. With hap_pi_ness my soul is cloyed— With
day of joy has bro_ken du - ly. With hap_pi_ness her soul is cloyed— With
day of joy has bro_ken du - ly. With hap_pi_ness her soul is cloyed— With
f
sempre p

cresc.
hap - pi-ness is cloyed— With hap-pi-ness my soul is cloyed— This is my joy-day un-al-
hap - pi-ness is cloyed— With hap-pi-ness her soul is cloyed— This is her joy-day un-al-
hap - pi-ness is cloyed— With hap-pi-ness her soul is cloyed— This is her joy-day un-al-
dim.
-loyed,— un-al-loyed, This is my joy - - - day un - al-loyed!
-loyed, un-al-loyed, This is her joy - - - day un - al-loyed!
-loyed,— un-al-loyed, This is her joy - - - day un - al-loyed!
rall.
a tempo
CHORUS.
Yes, yes, With
Yes, yes, With

Moderato marziale.
hap-pi-ness her soul is cloy-ed, This is her joy-day un-al-loyed!
hap-pi-ness her soul is cloy'd This is her joy-day un-al-loyed!,
Moderato marziale.
f
SOLO.
LIEUT.
Hold, pret-ty one! I bring to thee News-good or
p
ill, it is for thee to say. Thy hus-band
tr
tr

lives – and he is free, And comes to claim his bride this ve - ry
ff
Un poco meno mosso e agitato.
ELSIE.
day! No! no! re-call those words – it can-not be!
p
cresc. molto
f PHŒBE & DAME CARRUTHERS.
Oh, day of ter - ror! Oh, day of ter - ror!
f LIEUT, MERYLL & WILFRED.
Come, dry these un-be-com-ing tears, Most joy-ful ti-dings greet thine ears.
KATE & 1st & 2nd SOPS.
f
Oh, day of ter - ror! Oh, day of ter - ror!
TENORS & BASSES.
Oh, day of ter - ror! Oh, day of ter - ror!
8
Ped.
*

ELSIE.
Oh, Leo - nard,
PHŒBE & DAME.
The man to whom thou art al - lied
LIEUT, MERYLL & WILFRID.
Come, dry these un-be-com-ing tears, Most joy-ful ti-dings greet thine
Day of ter - - ror!
Day of ter - ror! day of tears!
Oh, Leo - nard,
Ap-pears to claim thee as his bride.
cars.
The man to whom thou art al-lied Ap-pears to claim thee as his
Day of ter - - ror!
Day of ter - ror! day of tears! Who is the

come thou to my side, And claim me
The man to whom thou art al - lied Ap - pears to
bride, The man to whom thou art al-lied Ap-pears to claim thee as his
Who is the man who in his pride claims thee
man who, in his pride claims thee
8
Ped.
as thy lov-ing bride. Day of ter - ror! day of tears!
claim thee as his bride. Day of ter - ror! day of tears!
bride as his bride?
bride as his bride?
as his bride? Day of ter - ror! day of tears!
as his bride? Day of ter - ror! day of tears!
f
3
3
Ped.

FAIRFAX. (sternly.)
All thought of Leo_nard Mer_yll
set a_side. Thou art mine own! I claim thee as my bride.
p
CHORUS.
Thou art his own, a_las, he claims thee as his bride!
Thou art his own, a_las, he claims thee as his bride!
RECIT.
ELSIE.
A
f
RECIT.
p
sup_pliant at thy feet I fall: Thine heart will yield to pi_ty's call!
FAIRFAX.
Mine is a

heart of mas_sive rock, Un_moved by sen_ti_men_tal shock!
CHORUS.
Thy hus_band
Thy hus_band
Andante espress. e con moto.
Con molto tenerezza.
ELSIE.
Leo_nard my loved one— come to me. They
he!
he!
Andante espress. e con moto.
dim.
Andante.
bear me_ hence a_way! But though they take me

far from thee My heart is thine for aye! My
bruis - ed heart, My bro - ken heart, Is thine, my own, for
aye! Is thine, is thine, my
appassionato
own, is thine, for aye!
cresc.
f
dim.
ff

Un poco più vivo.
Sir, I o-bey, I am thy bride; But ere the fa-tal hour I said the say That
placed me in thy pow'r, Would I had died! Sir, I o-bey! I am thy bride!
Allegro vivace e con fuoco.
FAIRFAX.
Leo - nard! My own!
ELSIE.
Ah! With hap - pi-ness my soul is cloyed,
FAIRFAX.
With hap - pi-ness my soul is cloyed,

This is our joy-day un-al-loyed!
This is our joy-day un-al-loyed!
sf
CHORUS.
Yes! yes! With hap-pi-ness their souls are cloyed,
Yes! yes! With hap-pi-ness their souls are cloyed,
This is their joy-day un-al-loyed! With
This is their joy-day un-al-loyed! With

hap - pi_ness their souls are cloyed, This is their joy - day un _ al _ loyed, their
hap - pi_ness their souls are cloyed, This is their joy - day un _ al _ loyed, their
joy - - day un - al - loyed,
joy - day un - al - loyed, un - - al - loyed!
joy - day un - al - loyed, un - - al - loyed!
8
pp
POINT.
Oh thought - less crew! Ye know not what ye
p
RECIT. (slower.)
rall.
do! At - tend to me, and shed a tear or two- For
rall.

A tempo I°
I have a song to sing, O!
CHORUS.
pp
dim.
Sing me your song, O!
pp
dim.
Sing me your song, O!
p
Ped.
POINT.
It is sung to the moon By a love-lorn loon, Who fled from the mocking throng, O! It's the
Ped.
Ped.
song of a mer-ry-man mop-ing mum, Whose soul was sad and whose glance was glum, Who
Ped.
Ped.
Ped.
sipped no sup and who craved no crumb, As he sighed for the love of a la-dye!
Ped.
Ped.
Ped.

Heigh - dy, Heigh - dy! Mis - e - ry me, lack-a-day-dee! He
Oo!
Oo!
sipped no sup and he craved no crumb, As he sighed for the love of a la - dye!
ELSIE.
I have a song to sing, O!
What is your song, O!
What is your song, O!

ELSIE.
It is sung with the ring Of the songs maids sing Who love with a love life-
-long, O! It's the song of a mer-ry-maid, nest-ling near Who loved her lord—but who
dropped a tear At the moan of the mer-ry-man mop-ing mum, Whose soul was sad and whose
glance was glum, Who sipp'd no sup and who craved no crumb, As he sigh'd for the love of a la-dye!

1st SOP. with ELSIE.
Heigh - dy! Heigh - dy! Mis-e-ry me, lack-a-day-dee! He
2nd SOPS.
p
Oo!
TEN. & BASS.
p
Oo!
sipped no sup and he craved no crumb, As he sighed for the love of a la - dye!
PHŒBE & DAME C with ELSIE.
f
cresc. e animato.
Heigh - dy! Heigh - dy! Mis-e-ry me, lack-a-day-dee! He
f
Oo!
f
Oo!
cresc. e animato.
f

cresc.
sipped no sup and he craved no crumb, As he sighed for the love of a la - dye!
cresc.
cresc.
TUTTI.
ff
Heigh - - - - - - - - dy!
Heigh -
Heigh - - - - - - - - dy!
Heigh -
ff
- - - - - dy!
Heigh - - - - - - -
- - - - - dy!
Heigh - - - - - -

END OF OPERA.

Printed and bound in Great Britain